Comprehension Test Prep

Setting · Main Idea · Supporting Details · Vocabulary · Figurative Language · Cause & Effect · Sequencing · Making Inferences · Drawing Conclusions

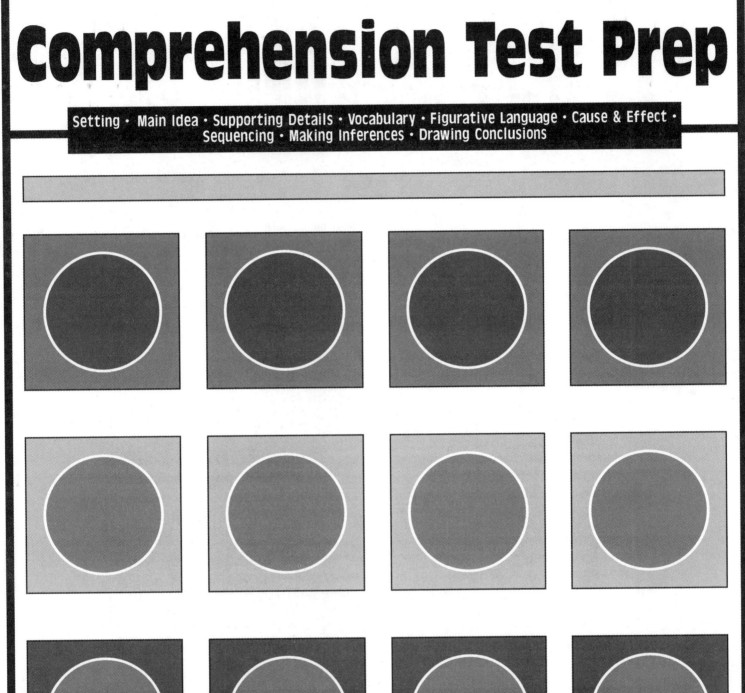

Written by Barbara Gregorich · Illustrated by Bev Armstrong

The Learning Works

The Learning Works

Editing, Typesetting, and Design: Clark Editorial & Design
Cover Illustrator: Rick Grayson
Cover Photographer: Ian Shaw/Getty Images
Cover Designer: Barbara Peterson

Contents

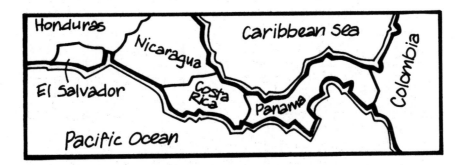

Comprehension Test Prep
© The Learning Works, Inc.

To the Teacher

Comprehension Test Prep has been written especially for use with students in grades 5-8. It combines high-interest reading material with challenging questions and activities to promote the development of specific reading skills.

The stories are grouped in three sections: Adventures, Mysteries, and Sports. Each story is followed by fifteen questions that cover the following skills:

1. Setting
2. Main Idea
3. Title
4-6. Supporting Details
7-9. Vocabulary
10. Figurative/Literal Language
11. Fact or Opinion
12-13. Cause and Effect
14. Sequence
15. Making Inferences/Drawing Conclusions

There are also suggestions for related activities in the areas of creative writing, drama, report writing, and research, and an answer key is provided for all questions that are not open-ended.

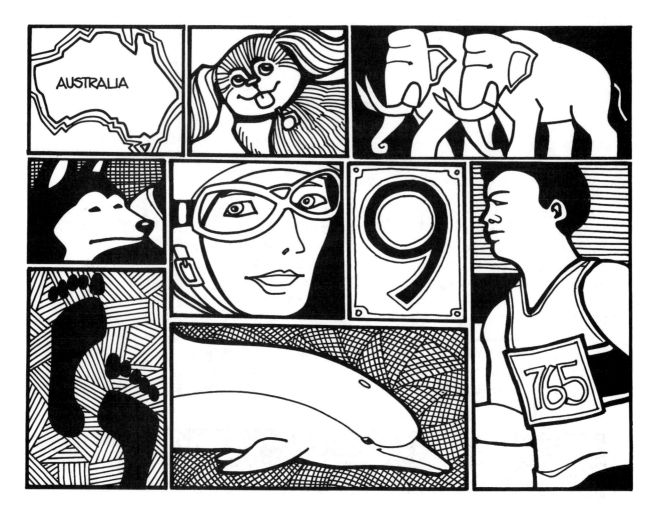

To the Student

The stories in this book will introduce you to new and exciting adventures, mysteries, and sports. The questions that follow each story will test specific skills, and answering them correctly will help you to improve your reading comprehension. Some of the information you will learn by answering these questions is as follows:

Setting — The setting of a story is the time and place in which it occurs. Clues within the story tell you when and where it happens. What verb tense is used? Are any dates mentioned? Could events described in the story have occurred only in the past? Could they happen now or in the future? What kinds of clothing are the characters wearing? What sorts of activities do they engage in? Are they indoors or outdoors? Is the story set in a particular city, town, country, or other geographical area? How does the setting affect the story?

Main Idea — The main idea of a story is the point that the author is trying to make in telling it. Although the main idea often can be expressed in a single sentence, it is more than simply what the story is about. For example, a statement such as, "This story is about baseball," names the subject of the story — baseball — but does not describe the main idea. What is the author trying to say about baseball? On the other hand, a statement such as, "This story is about the importance of having a good third baseman during a critical baseball game," says it all.

Title — The title is the name an author gives to a story. It may be a brief description, a pun, or a thought-provoking question. Sometimes a title summarizes the main idea of a story, and its meaning is easy to understand. Other times, a title can be understood only after you have read the story and thought about it for a while.

Supporting Details — To write the text for any story, you need a topic, or a main idea, and you need the details to support, or explain, that idea. Supporting details are the individual facts in a story that help to make the main idea understood. They clarify your meaning and complete the word picture you are trying to create. They answer the questions who, what, when, where, why, how, what kind, and how many.

Vocabulary — Your vocabulary is the total number of words that you know well enough to use correctly. The larger your vocabulary, the easier it will be for you to say exactly what you mean. In this book, vocabulary questions will test your knowledge of word meanings and word constructions. When you are asked to give the meaning of a word, define it as precisely as possible. Put the word in a category, then show how it is different from the other members of that category. For example, how would you define the word crawl when used in reference to swimming? To categorize crawl, you could write: "The crawl is a way of swimming." Next, you could explain how it differs from other ways of swimming: "The crawl is a way of swimming in which the swimmer lies on her stomach and moves forward along the surface of the water by using alternate overarm strokes and continuous flutter kicks."

Comprehension Test Prep
© The Learning Works, Inc.

To the Student

(continued)

Figurative/Literal Language — Figurative language is any language that is used creatively and imaginatively to evoke vivid images and give fresh insights. To answer questions about figurative language, you must first understand the difference between two antonyms — literal and figurative. Literal means "actual, real." Figurative means "not literal; expressing one thing in terms normally used to denote or describe another." Figurative language makes actions and speech more vivid. For example, if Liz literally went through the roof, she probably fell through it while installing an antenna or making a repair, and she ended up on the living room floor. If, on the other hand, Liz figuratively went through the roof, she probably yelled, shouted, screamed, gestured, and otherwise carried on in an angry fashion, but she really went nowhere.

Fact or Opinion — A fact is a statement that has been or can be proved to be true; an opinion is a belief, evaluation, feeling, estimation, or judgment. It is a fact that lacrosse is a sport played with a ball and a stick. It is an opinion that lacrosse is the most exciting sport in the world.

Cause and Effect — A cause is the reason an event occurs; an effect is what happens as a result of that event. Cause: You throw a rock into a small pond. Possible effects: Ripples and splashes. One cause may have many effects. For example, you could throw the rock hard enough to wrench your shoulder. Some effects are observable, while others are not. For example, it is easy to see wet clothes on the bystanders and ripples on the pond, but you might never notice the effects that the sinking rock has below the surface of the water.

Sequence — All events happen in a definite order. This order is called a sequence. Events may be ordered chronologically, or they may be arranged according to their cause-and-effect relationships. When you are asked to put events in chronological order, list them according to the time or order in which they actually occurred.

Making Inferences/Drawing Conclusions — An inference is an educated guess based on facts or premises. A conclusion is a final judgment based on more concrete or persuasive evidence. In creating an inference, one uses reasoning to come up with a judgment or fact based on the information that is available.

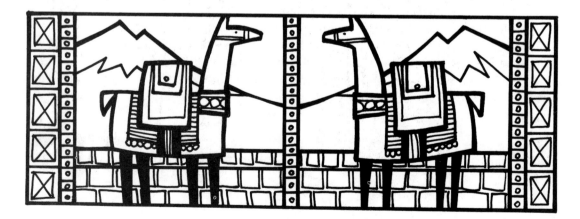

Reading Skills Chart

Use the chart on page 8 to keep track of your reading skills development. After the questions about a particular story have been graded, find that story title on the chart and shade in the number of each question that you got right. Then enter the date and your score (the total number of questions you got right out of fifteen) at the end of that row.

When you have read all eighteen stories, count the number of shaded boxes under each question number and enter that number as a total for each column. Check yourself by adding the score column, adding the numbers of shaded boxes, and comparing these two sums. They should be the same.

Analyze the results. Have your scores improved since you first began reading these stories and answering the questions? Look at the shaded boxes. Do you regularly miss the same kinds of questions? If so, you could probably use some additional practice to help you develop the specific reading skills to which these questions relate.

Comprehension Test Prep
© The Learning Works, Inc.

Reading Skills Chart

Story Title	Pages	Setting (1)	Main Idea (2)	Title (3)	Supporting Details (4)	Supporting Details (5)	Supporting Details (6)	Vocabulary (7)	Vocabulary (8)	Vocabulary (9)	Figurative/Literal Language (10)	Fact or Opinion (11)	Cause and Effect (12)	Cause and Effect (13)	Sequence (14)	Making Inferences/Drawing Conclusions (15)	Date	Score
Adventures	**9-21**																	
Ninety North!	9-11																	
Lifeboat Aquarius	12-13																	
Frozen in Time	14-15																	
Life on the Moon	16-17																	
They Traveled Far	18-19																	
From Failure to Success	20-21																	
Mysteries	**22-35**																	
Clever Hans	22-24																	
The Disappearing Emerald	25-26																	
Into Thin Air	27-29																	
The Big Bang	30-31																	
Aquatic Talkers?	32-33																	
A Mystery Solved?	34-35																	
Sports	**36-50**																	
26.218	36-38																	
Two Kinds of Skiing	39-41																	
Night of Dreams	42-43																	
What a Game!	44-45																	
Mush Against Death	46-48																	
The Last Lap	49-50																	
Totals																		

Name_____

Ninety North!

Young Robert Peary loved the outdoors of Maine, his native state. The only child of a widow, he sought to excel at whatever he did. Baseball, track, rowing — he was an accomplished athlete in all of these sports. Science, theory, poetry — he won scholarships and graduated second in his college class. Then he entered the U.S. Navy and became Lt. Robert Peary. Soon the young officer was sent into the jungles of Nicaragua to help survey the land for what might one day be a canal connecting the Atlantic and Pacific Oceans.

Robert Peary enjoyed his work, but he longed to do something extraordinary, to perform some deed or feat that would live long after he was gone. Suddenly, while on assignment in Greenland, it came to him: he, Robert Peary, would be the first man to stand at the North Pole! The Eskimos, who liked this man and called him "Pearyaksoah," ("Big Peary" in their language) thought he was crazy. What was the sense, they asked, in going to the North Pole, an icy, barren speck in the middle of the Arctic Ocean? It was, after all, no different from any other place in the middle of that frozen wilderness. But if Peary was crazy, it was with the dream of immortality. He knew that the first man to reach that spot would have eternal fame. "Ninety North!" became his motto.

By 1905, Peary had tried to reach Ninety North five times, and each time he had failed. The temperature usually hovered around 30 degrees below zero, the wind blew relentlessly, and frostbite was a constant danger. Peary had already suffered the amputation of eight toes because of frostbite. However, his five attempts had won him countless fans around the world.

In 1905, when he was fifty years old, Robert Peary tried again. Around his body he wore an American flag woven from silk; as he fought the ice and snow, he dreamed of unfurling that flag at the North Pole. But the closer he got to Ninety North, the colder it became — 40, 50, 60, 70 degrees below zero. At the same time, his men and dogs were starving. When only 170 miles south of the Pole, they all turned back. Disheartened, Peary felt that he had tried to reach the North Pole for the last time. Then four years later, he tried once again. On April 6, 1909, he reached his goal: Ninety North — and immortality!

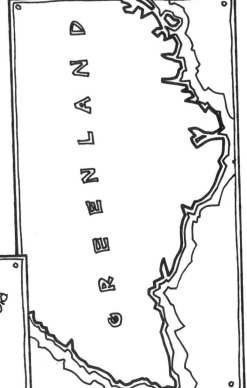

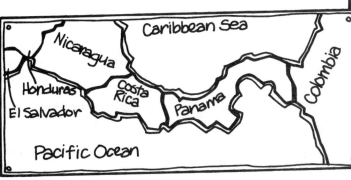

Comprehension Test Prep
© The Learning Works, Inc.

Name _____

Ninety North!
(continued)

Write the correct answer for each question.

1. Approximately when was Robert Peary born? _____

2. What is the main idea of this story? _____
   _____
   _____

3. How does the title of the story relate to the main idea? _____
   _____
   _____

4. What did the Eskimos call Peary and what did it mean? _____
   _____

5. How low had the temperature plunged when Peary turned back in 1905? _____

6. Where was Peary when he first decided to pursue his goal? _____

7. What does the word **native** mean in the first sentence of the story? _____
   _____

8. What does the word **relentlessly** mean in the third paragraph? _____

9. The word **sought** is used in the first paragraph. It is the past tense of a verb. Write the present tense of that verb and a synonym for it._____

10. Did Peary achieve immortality literally or figuratively? _____
    Explain your answer. _____
    _____
    _____

11. Peary had one opinion about the possibility of reaching the North Pole, and the Eskimos had another. How did their opinions differ? _____
    _____
    _____
    _____

Name _____

Ninety North!
(continued)

12. What caused Peary to turn back in 1905? _____

_____

13. How did Peary's failure in 1905 affect him psychologically?_____

_____

_____

14. The names of four places are listed below. Write them in order according to when Peary visited each place: Nicaragua, North Pole, Maine, Greenland._____

_____

15. What conclusions about Robert Peary's character can you draw from this story? _____

_____

_____

_____

Related Activities

- Write a one-act play based on Robert Peary's adventurous life.
- Like Robert Peary, Richard Byrd was an officer in the U.S. Navy and a polar explorer. Find out more about Byrd; then write a paragraph or two in which you compare these two men.

Name_____

Lifeboat Aquarius

Imagine driving along a country road in the middle of the night, miles from the nearest service station. Suddenly, you feel a great bump! Your car's body vibrates. Scary? Certainly! But your fright would be mild compared to the fear experienced by Fred Haise, James Lovell, and John Swigert on Monday, April 13, 1970. More than 200,000 nautical miles from home, hurtling at 18,000 miles per hour in space blacker than any night, the three astronauts felt a tremendous bump in their spaceship.

What caused it? Surely they had not run into anything out in the middle of space! Yet the ship was shaking from that bump, and the needles on the instrument panel were spinning out of control. The three men looked at one another. Something was seriously wrong with *Apollo 13*, now two days out in space.

After a thorough investigation, the astronauts determined that a fuel cell was not functioning properly. A mysterious explosion had blown off a solar panel and left the command ship, called *Odyssey*, unable to generate power or produce and pump oxygen. Frantically, NASA officials at Mission Control in Houston, Texas, tried to decide what to do. After considering the alternatives, they came up with the best possible solution: Haise, Lovell, and Swigert were ordered to forget about landing on the moon. Instead, they were to shut down all power in the command module and climb into *Aquarius*, the lunar module. The astronauts had intended to use *Aquarius* as a lunar lander. Now they would have to use it as a lifeboat.

The astronauts turned off all the fuel supplies in the command ship. They had to save the scant ten hours of operating life it had left so that it could return to earth. They had no heat, no light, no water, and no filters to clean the air of mildly poisonous gases. Without heat, the temperature in the command module dropped as low as 30 degrees. Haise, Lovell, and Swigert crawled into *Aquarius*. For more than three days, the men lived in this lifeboat much like three hermit crabs squeezed into one shell. When they reached the earth's reentry field, they abandoned *Aquarius* and returned to *Odyssey*. They knew that although the lunar module could not withstand the heat of reentry, the command module could.

Back inside the larger spacecraft, the astronauts jettisoned *Aquarius*, the spacecraft that had been their lifeboat for more than eighty hours. Then they brought their command ship down for the most accurate landing in the history of manned space flight. The astronauts were cold, hungry, and dirty, but thanks to their ingenuity, resourcefulness, and courage, they were safe!

Write the correct answers on the lines.

1. When did the events described in this story occur? _____

_____

2. In one sentence, write the main idea of this story. _____

_____

_____

Name _____

Lifeboat Aquarius
(continued)

3. Write another possible title for this story. _____

4. What was the name and number of the space flight? _____

5. Write the last names of the three astronauts. _____

   _____

6. At what speed was the spacecraft traveling when the astronauts felt the bump? _____

   _____

7. What word in the fourth paragraph means "forsook; gave up forever; deserted?" _____

   _____

8. In the first paragraph, does **tremendous** mean "wonderful" or "enormous"? _____

   _____

9. There are three compound words in the fourth paragraph that are not hyphenated. Write them here.

   _____   _____   _____

10. The fourth paragraph contains a simile. Write it here. _____

    _____

    _____

    From the words listed below, choose the correct ones to write on the lines.

    affects   causes   fact   perfectly
    before   effects   opinion   when

11. It is a _____ that *Aquarius* could not withstand the heat of reentry.

12. One of the _____ of turning off the power in the command ship was that the astronauts became cold, hungry, and dirty.

13. One of the _____ of the astronauts' moving into *Aquarius* was that a fuel cell on *Apollo 13* was not functioning properly.

14. The astronauts abandoned *Aquarius* and returned to *Odyssey* _____ they reached the earth's reentry field.

15. After reading this story, you could conclude that no machinery can be guaranteed to work

    _____ .

Related Activity

- Imagine that you are one of the astronauts on this mission. Write a journal entry for April 13, 1970.

13

Name_____

Frozen in Time

High in the Andes mountains in Argentina along the Chilean border, U.S. archaeologist Dr. Johan Reinhard and a team of Peruvian scientists struggled in frigid conditions to climb Mount Llullaillaco, a volcano, 22,100 feet (6,700 meters) high. They battled whipping winds, drifting snow, and nearly unbearable conditions to hunt for mummies frozen in time — ice mummies.

This extraordinary expedition to one of the highest archaeological sites in the world took place in March of 1999. Reinhard, one of the world's foremost authorities of high-altitude archaeology, has been climbing the breathtaking Andes for twenty years. He said he decided to search this particular area because he had read that Incan ruins had been found on the volcano.

The work of excavating the site was back-breaking, and digging in frozen rock proved difficult. Then, the tension grew as one of the team members was lowered upside down by his ankles into a six foot (1.8 meter) deep, dark pit. Minutes later, they pulled out the scientist who was cradling a mummy in his arms. He was holding the frozen body of an Inca girl buried 500 years ago. Eventually, the team unearthed a total of three frozen bodies — two girls and a boy who died between the ages of 8 and 15 years old.

Ice mummies are bodies preserved in extreme cold. Freezing conditions almost totally halt the decay of a corpse's body tissues. Most bacteria and fungi that normally rot dead bodies can't survive in subfreezing climates. These three ice mummies were the best-preserved mummies ever discovered from South America's Inca civilization. Tests revealed blood still frozen in their hearts and lungs and their internal organs intact.

The ice mummies discovered by Reinhard may have been buried in the snow on purpose as an offering to the Sun God. The team of scientists also found offerings to the Inca gods, including gold, silver and sea-shell statues, and ornate woven and embroidered textiles, moccasins and pottery, some still containing food.

Scientists expect the Inca ice mummies to give them a glimpse into the past before the Spanish conquest in 1532. Techniques like DNA analysis (analysis of genetic material) and an x-ray procedure called computed tomography (CT) scanning can determine a mummy's diseases, its last meal, and perhaps even the cause of death. Scientists can even use genetic information to determine their ancestry by comparing blood samples and DNA from the mummies with blood and DNA of modern people.

Write the correct answer for each question.

1. How long ago is it believed that the ice mummies were buried? _____

2. What is the main idea of this story? _____

   _____

3. Write another possible title for this story._____

4. What did the team of scientists find at the burial site in the Andes?_____

   _____

Name_____

Frozen in Time
(continued)

5. Where is Mt. Llullaillaco located? _____
_____

6. Who is the world's foremost authority of high-altitude archaeology? _____
_____

7. **Archaeology** is the study of _____

8. What is meant by the term **offerings** in the fifth paragraph? _____
_____

9. What are **bacteria**? _____
_____

10. What does the description "battled whipping winds" mean? _____
_____

11. Is it fact or opinion that the mummies were an offering to the Sun God? _____

12. What is the effect of freezing conditions on bacteria and fungi? _____
_____

13. What caused Dr. Johan Reinhard to take an archaeological expedition to Mount Llullaillaco?
_____

14. Put these events in chronological order: a mummy of a child is found in the Andes; scientists climb Mt. Llullaillaco; scientists use DNA to study the mummies; scientists dig through frozen rock. _____
_____
_____
_____

15. In your opinion, why does Dr. Reinhard practice archaeology in places like the Andes?
_____
_____
_____

Related Activities

- Learn about other ice mummies such as the Greenland mummies from Qilakitsoq; "Juanita," another Inca mummy; or the Siberian Ice Maiden. Write a short story about one of them.
- The Incan empire lasted only 90 years. Learn more about the Incan empire. Draw a picture of one interesting aspect of Incan culture.

Name_____

Life on the Moon

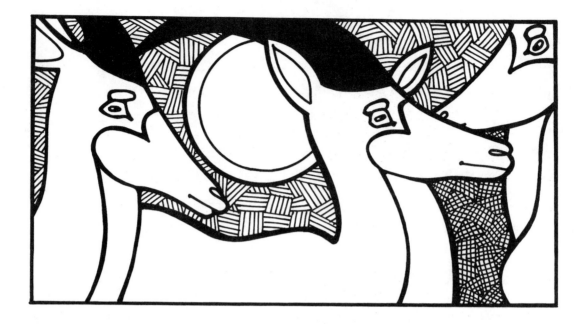

On August 25, 1835, the *New York Sun* announced that famed British astronomer Sir John Herschel had made history from his new observatory at the Cape of Good Hope in Africa. Journalist Richard Adams Locke wrote that Herschel had constructed "a telescope of vast dimensions using an entirely new principle."

According to Locke, on January 18, 1835, at precisely 9:30 P.M. African time, Herschel reportedly looked through his telescope and saw basalt (a type of rock), yews (a class of trees), and a huge sea or lake, its waters bright blue. Readers were astounded! Was it possible? Life on the moon! Who would have believed it? Apparently, thousands of people did, and why not? After all, this was the age of scientific miracles. If steamboats and railroads were possible, then why not a powerful new telescope that revealed life on the moon?

The *New York Sun* articles continued daily. Locke wrote that Herschel had seen buffalo-like animals on the moon, including a bluish, goat-like animal with a single horn on its head. And then, wonder of wonders, subsequent issues of the paper reported that there were winged people on the moon! These winged beings were copper-colored, about four feet tall, and covered with hair.

Locke's articles not only became the talk of New York, but also captured the imagination of the entire United States. Unfortunately, nothing in the articles was true. Sir John Herschel, working in Africa, was actually unaware of these reports, his supposed findings, and even of Richard Adams Locke. The entire series was a fabrication. Once the hoax was exposed, Locke claimed he meant it as satire — writing that pokes fun at something — of astronomers. Perhaps this is true, but the fact is that his articles, presented as news stories, increased the circulation of the *New York Sun* significantly. Within a week of the start of the series, the *Sun* boasted the largest circulation of any newspaper on earth — or on the moon, for that matter!

Name_____

Life on the Moon

(continued)

Write the correct answers on the lines.

1. In what year did the series of newspaper articles appear?_____

2. What is the main idea of this story? _____
   _____
   _____

3. Why is the title of the story misleading? _____
   _____

4. Who was the astronomer in question? _____

5. On what date did he reportedly make his first moon discovery? _____

6. Who was the journalist involved? _____

7. What word in the third paragraph means "coming after; following in time or order"?_____
   _____

8. What is a **hoax**? _____
   _____

9. In the last paragraph, the noun **fabrication** comes from the verb **fabricate**. Write the noun form of a similarly constructed word in the same paragraph. _____
   What is its verb form? _____

10. What does the expression **wonder of wonders** mean? _____

Write T if a statement is true. Write F if it is false.

_____11. It is a fact that the *New York Sun* reported that Herschel had discovered life on the moon.

_____12. According to Locke, Herschel was able to see animals on the moon because he had constructed a new and more powerful telescope.

_____13. The effect of Locke's articles was that the circulation of the *New York Sun* decreased.

_____14. According to the articles, Herschel saw the copper-colored people before he saw the yews and basalt.

_____15. Based on the facts of this story, one can conclude that many people love to read astounding news.

Related Activity

• Imagine that you are an unethical newspaper reporter. You want to perpetrate a hoax that the sun will explode within a year. Write the story, but remember that it must be believable.

Name_____

They Traveled Far

Nellie Bly and Blanche Stuart Scott were adventuresome women. Nellie Bly was the pen name of Elizabeth Cochrane who was born in 1867 near Pittsburgh, Pennsylvania. At the age of eighteen, Cochrane wrote a letter to the editor of the newspaper *Pittsburgh Dispatch* in response to an article entitled "What Girls Are Good For." In her letter, Cochrane defended the rights of women. George Madden, the author of the article, liked her writing so much that he offered the young woman a job. She promptly accepted, and she adopted Nellie Bly as her pseudonym.

Bly wrote about slums, sweatshops, and corruption in government. There was no assignment she would not tackle. Once she even pretended to be insane and had herself committed to a mental hospital. After her release, she wrote a series of articles about the horrible conditions in insane asylums. Her articles helped initiate reforms in mental institutions.

Although Bly wrote many articles and had many adventures, she is perhaps most famous for her trip around the world. Nellie Bly announced this trip in 1889, claiming she would circle the globe in seventy-five days, five days fewer than Jules Verne's fictional hero, Phileas Fogg, took to complete a similar journey in *Around the World in Eighty Days*. People laughed at the notion of circling the colossal world in so short a time. Six months, maybe, but seventy-five days? Nellie Bly did it, though, completing her journey in a few hours less than seventy-three days!

Just about the time Nellie Bly was beginning her first job, another adventurer was born in Rochester, New York. Blanche Stuart Scott was known as "a terror" in her time. In a period when girls were supposed to act like "young ladies," Scott decided to become a trick bicyclist. She wrecked many bicycles (and nearly wrecked herself) while learning.

Once Scott had mastered cycling, she became a champion ice skater. Next, she got a job selling automobiles. From there it seemed a logical step to drive across the country in an automobile. This was a terribly exciting feat for the time, but it was not exciting enough for Blanche Stuart Scott. No, this determined young woman decided she would become a stunt pilot! By this time, it seemed that Blanche Scott could do just about anything. Scott later became a stunt pilot, a test pilot, an actress, a writer, and a radio commentator. She and Nellie Bly traveled a long way down the trail of challenge and adventure.

Circle the letter of the best answer.

1. The period in which Bly and Scott lived was roughly
   a. 1800-1900.   b. 1850-1950.   c. 1900-2000.

2. The main idea of this story is that Bly and Scott were
   a. improper.   b. women.   c. travelers.

3. Another title for this story could be
   a. "Bly and Cochrane."
   b. "Men and Women."
   c. "Across the Country and Around the World."

Name_____

They Traveled Far
(continued)

4. Scott was born
    a. in Rochester, New York.   b. near Pittsburgh, Pennsylvania.   c. in 1867.

5. Bly made her famous trip
    a. in a balloon.   b. in 1889.   c. in eighty days.

Write the correct answers on the lines.

6. How old was Cochrane when she was offered a job as a reporter?_____

7. What term in the first paragraph is a synonym for **pseudonym**? _____

8. What does **colossal** mean? _____

9. There are two compound words in the first paragraph that are not hyphenated. Write them
    here._____

10. What does the expression **circle the globe** mean?_____

11. When people called young Blanche Stuart Scott "a terror," were they expressing a fact or an
    opinion? _____

12. What was the effect of Elizabeth Cochrane's letter to the editor? _____
    _____

13. What caused her to write the letter? _____
    _____
    _____

14. Name four things Scott did after becoming a trick bicycle rider? _____
    _____
    _____

15. What can you infer about the character of people such as Bly and Scott? _____
    _____
    _____

Related Activity
- Write a song or poem about the adventures of Nellie Bly, Blanche Stuart Scott, or both.

Comprehension Test Prep
© The Learning Works, Inc.

Name_____

From Failure to Success

The 1804–1806 journey of Meriwether Lewis and William Clark through the wilderness of the northwestern United States encouraged many others to follow their example. Trading companies vied with one another in exploring, staking out the best lands, building forts, and trading with Native Americans for furs. It was one such company, the North West Company of Canada, that sent a young man named Simon Fraser to explore the Columbia River to its mouth.

In 1807, Fraser started his journey into the unknown, hoping to reach the mouth of the Columbia through its upper waters. He planned to explore the river all the way to the Pacific Ocean, thinking that he and his company could claim all of the land to the north of latitude 46°20' north. This, according to Lewis and Clark, was the precise location of the river's mouth.

Fraser and his men, either paddling canoes or carrying them overland — a method called portage — made their way through a maze of forested mountains, swift rivers, and icy lakes. As they continued their journey along the stream that Fraser assumed to be the upper Columbia, travel was no less perilous. Danger was all around as they rode rushing water through narrow canyons, surrounded on all sides by steep cliffs. In many places, the river suddenly foamed into rapids that tossed the frail canoes treacherously close to the rock walls.

More than once, the explorers found themselves trapped in canyons where the river was not navigable. Then they had to chop steps into the towering walls and with their canoes and supplies, climb up the cliff face. Following the edge of the chasm, they continued downstream by portage until they reached a place where they could return to the stream and paddle again.

At last Fraser caught sight of open water ahead. The river emptied into a broad bay. His weary heart beat faster at the sight. Success was at hand! Then he measured the angle of the sun. Impossible! His reading was not latitude 46°20', but 49° north. He had explored the wrong river! His mission had failed.

Happily, Fraser's "failure" turned into an unexpected success. The great river he had explored was named for him, and today the Fraser River is the most important river in British Columbia. It is the spawning ground of the commercially valuable Pacific salmon. The Fraser River also helps create the most fertile land in British Columbia, and its delta is home to many dairy farms.

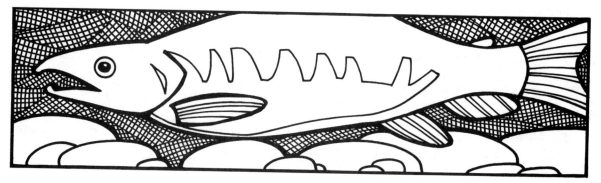

Name_____

From Failure to Success
(continued)

Write the correct answer for each question.

1. When did the events in this story take place?_____

2. What is the main idea of this story? _____

   _____

   _____

3. Write another title for the story. _____

   _____

Write the letter of the correct answer on the line in front of each number.

_____4. Fraser ended his journey at

_____5. The mouth of the Columbia was at

_____6. The Fraser River is in

_____7. A river upon which a boat can travel is

_____8. An activity filled with risks or danger is

A. British Columbia.

B. perilous.

C. 46°20' N.

D. 49° N.

E. navigable.

Write the correct answer for each question.

9. The past tense of a three-letter word meaning "to enter in competition with" appears in the first paragraph. Write both the past and present tense of this verb._____

10. A **paradox** is a statement that seems to contradict itself. What is the paradox in the last paragraph? _____

    _____

11. Does the statement, "He had explored the wrong river!" express fact or opinion? _____

12. What was the cause of Fraser's journey?_____

    _____

13. What was the effect of his journey? _____

    _____

14. Name two men who journeyed to the northwest before Fraser. _____

    _____

15. What conclusions can you reach about Fraser's character? _____

    _____

Related Activity

- Sir Alexander Mackenzie was a famous Scottish explorer of Canada who, like Fraser, discovered a river which was later named for him. Read about Mackenzie's exploits, and write a 250- to 300-word report about them.

Comprehension Test Prep
© The Learning Works, Inc.

To the Root of the Mystery of Clever Hans

"Hans, what is the square root of nine?" Tap, tap, tap. To the amazement of the German audience, Clever Hans solved a series of math problems. What was most remarkable was that the tapped answers were made with a hoof. Clever Hans was a stallion.

Hans' owner, Herr von Osten, had a hypothesis that animals are as intelligent as humans. After working unsuccessfully with a cat and a bear, he decided to try to train a horse. Herr von Osten believed his path to immortality was assured when he taught Hans to tap out correct answers to problems written on a board. Herr von Osten brought Hans before a panel of scientists to demonstrate his discovery.

The scientists tried in vain to discredit Herr von Osten, believing he must be giving Hans the answers through trickery or visual clues. To test this, they had Herr von Osten leave the room, certain that Hans would fail without his master there to cue him. They were stymied when Clever Hans still solved the problems almost every time.

One scientist, however, was even cleverer than Hans. He made sure that no one in the room could see the problem and, therefore, knew the answer. Under these circumstances, Hans failed every time.

The scientists theorized that Hans was probably able to sense subtle clues — a nod of the head, a tensing of the shoulders, a lifting of an eyebrow — that observers gave when Hans was about to tap out the correct answer. Thus, Hans knew when to stop tapping when he saw these clues. This phenomenon, called "The Clever Hans Syndrome," taught scientists the importance of "double blind" experiments — experiments in which the testers do not know the correct answers so they cannot inadvertently tip off the subjects of the experiment. Herr von Osten never was able to prove that animals are as smart as humans, but with the naming of "The Clever Hans Syndrome," his horse ultimately left his hoof print on scientific history!

Name_____

To the Root of the Mystery of Clever Hans
(continued)

Write the correct answer.

1. In what country did Herr von Osten live? _____

Circle the letter of the best answer.

2. What is the main idea of this story?

    a. Animals can be taught to think like humans.

    b. Horses are smarter than cats or bears.

    c. Scientific results can be affected by unanticipated factors.

    d. Double blind experiments are used to test intelligence.

Write the correct answer for each question.

3. What word play is there in the title of this story?_____
_____

4. What did Herr von Osten believe about animals?_____
_____

5. How did scientists try to make sure that Herr von Osten wasn't giving Hans answers to problems? _____
_____

6. Under what circumstances did Hans show he couldn't really solve the problems? _____
_____

7. In the second paragraph, what is the meaning of the word **hypothesis**? _____
_____

8. In the third paragraph, what is the meaning of the word **stymied**? _____
_____

9. In the fifth paragraph, what is the meaning of the word **subtle**? _____
_____

Comprehension Test Prep
© The Learning Works, Inc.

Name_____

To the Root of the Mystery of Clever Hans
(continued)

Write the correct answer for each question.

10. In the last sentence, is the phrase "Hans left his hoof print on scientific history" a literal or a figurative phrase? _____

11. Is it fact or opinion that Herr von Osten thought Hans could solve math problems?_____

12. What caused the scientists to send Herr von Osten from the room? _____
_____

13. What was the effect of "The Clever Hans Syndrome" on scientific research? _____
_____

14. Put these events in chronological order, from first to last:

_____a. Herr von Osten had Hans perform his tricks for scientists.

_____b. Hans could not perform the problems when no one in the room knew the answers.

_____c. Herr von Osten taught Hans to tap out answers to problems.

_____d. Herr von Osten decides to try training a horse.

15. What conclusions could you draw about whether Herr von Osten intended to trick the scientific community about animals' ability to think and reason? _____
_____

Related Activities

• Find out about other animals that can communicate with humans in nonverbal ways.

• Find out about other animals that seem to have used their intelligence to solve problems — monkeys, elephants, and dogs, for example.

Name_____

The Disappearing Emerald

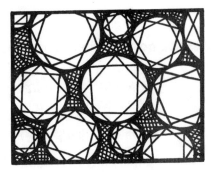

As the jeweler watched the street from the confines of his establishment, he noticed an elegantly dressed woman step out of a carriage. Her gown was brocade, and her cloak was trimmed in ermine to match the muff she carried to warm her hands. The driver handed the lady a dog — one of those yapping creatures that seek to make up in volume for what they lack in size. As the lady, now leading her pet on a leash, rang the bell of his exclusive shop, the jeweler eagerly let her in.

An hour later, his eagerness had faded. The lady had studied appreciatively each tray of gems set on the counter before her, but after each survey, she had shaken her head and asked to see another tray. "Was she here to buy," the jeweler wondered to himself, "or merely to browse?" Finally, she asked to see tray number thirteen one more time. Inwardly, the jeweler rejoiced, as that particular tray contained his most expensive stones. Then, as he was placing the tray on the counter, it happened. Gingerly reaching forward, with an exclamation of delight, the lady upset the tray. Bright stones scattered everywhere. The lady cried out in agitation, the jeweler moaned in dismay, and the dog yipped shrilly in accompaniment.

Scurrying about, the jeweler picked up the fallen stones. The lady tried to help him, though he would have preferred that she did not. Indeed, between trying to help him and soothing her nervous pet with little pieces of biscuit drawn from her silk purse, she was more of a hindrance than a help. As the jeweler gathered up the last of the gems, he realized something that made his heart stop: his prized Krucha emerald was missing! Frantically, he searched the floor again, but to no avail. Then his eyes settled suspiciously on the lady. Somewhat reluctantly, he called the police.

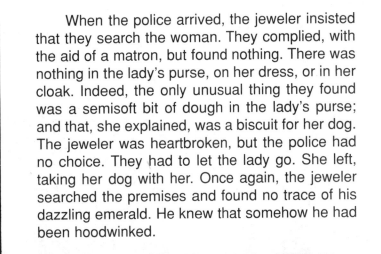

When the police arrived, the jeweler insisted that they search the woman. They complied, with the aid of a matron, but found nothing. There was nothing in the lady's purse, on her dress, or in her cloak. Indeed, the only unusual thing they found was a semisoft bit of dough in the lady's purse; and that, she explained, was a biscuit for her dog. The jeweler was heartbroken, but the police had no choice. They had to let the lady go. She left, taking her dog with her. Once again, the jeweler searched the premises and found no trace of his dazzling emerald. He knew that somehow he had been hoodwinked.

Name_____

The Disappearing Emerald
(continued)

From the words listed below, choose the correct ones to write on the lines.

diamond   ermine   jewels   past
dough   future   lady   summarizes
emerald   jeweler   mink   tray

1. This story takes place in the _____ .

2. The main idea is that, after a _____ overturns a _____ of _____ , a valuable _____ is missing.

3. The title _____ the main idea of the story.

4. The lady kept _____ in her purse.

5. The lady wore a muff of _____ .

Write the correct answer for each question.

6. What was the number of the tray the lady asked to see again?_____

7. In the third paragraph, what does the word **soothing** mean? _____

8. What does the word **gingerly** mean in the second paragraph? _____

9. Analyze the word **hoodwink**. What are its parts?_____
    What does it mean?_____

10. "The jeweler realized something that made his heart stop." Is this statement literal or figurative? _____ How do you know? _____
    _____

11. Is it a fact or an opinion that the jeweler had been hoodwinked?_____

12. What caused the stones to scatter? _____
    _____

13. What effect did the falling gems have on the dog?_____
    _____

14. Put the jeweler's feelings in sequence: dismay, jubilation, eagerness, suspicion. _____
    _____

15. In what season of the year does the story take place?_____
    How do you know? _____
    _____
    _____

Related Activity

- Continue writing this short story. Bring it to a conclusion that explains what happened to the emerald.

Name_____

Into Thin Air

Amelia Earhart was ten years old when she saw her first airplane, but she was unimpressed. "It was a thing of rusty wire and wood and not at all interesting," she thought. Her opinion changed when she attended an aerial exhibition in 1920. Her interest in flying was piqued. The next day, she flew in an open cockpit biplane for a ten-minute flight over Los Angeles. Amelia was hooked on flying.

Amelia took flying lessons and then purchased an airplane of her own. Soon she was piloting planes and breaking records. Her name became a household word. In 1932, she became the first woman to make a solo journey across the Atlantic.

In 1937, at the age of 40, Amelia Earhart decided to embark on her most ambitious and dangerous flight. She set out to fly around the world. She knew the trip might be perilous, but she said, "I want to do it because I want to do it. Women must try to do things as men have tried. When they fail, their failure must be but a challenge to others."

Earhart and her navigator Fred Noonan left Miami on June 1, 1937, their Electra 10E piercing the clouds towards a place in history. They flew to South America, across Africa, and on to India. Battling bad weather and illness, they arrived in New Guinea on June 29, 1937. They had almost completed their journey, with the balance of the trip to be flown over the Pacific Ocean.

On July 2, Earhart and Noonan took off for Howland Island, approximately 2,500 miles away. The initial radio transmissions indicated that they were on course. The next signals were too brief and too weak to pinpoint a location for the plane. Then there was silence. A mighty rescue attempt proved unsuccessful.

No one knows what really happened to Amelia Earhart. Some people think her plane crashed and she perished at sea. Others believe she landed safely on an island in the South Pacific. No evidence of the plane or its passengers was ever found. The mystery of Amelia Earhart's last flight remains unsolved.

Name_____

Into Thin Air
(continued)

Write the correct answer.

1. When was Amelia Earhart born?_____

Circle the letter of the best answer.

2. The main idea of this story is:

    a. Amelia Earhart was not interested in flying until she took flying lessons.

    b. Flying is dangerous.

    c. Amelia Earhart disappeared in her attempt to fly around the world.

    d. Earhart and Noonan were an experienced flying team.

Write the correct answer for each question.

3. Explain the meaning of the title. _____

_____

4. What did Earhart think of the first airplane she saw? _____

_____

5. Where did Amelia Earhart's last flight begin? _____

6. How far did Earhart get in her flight around the world?_____

_____

7. In the first paragraph, what is the meaning of the word **piqued**?_____

_____

8. In the third paragraph, explain the meaning of the word **perilous**._____

_____

Circle the letter of the best answer.

9. In the fifth paragraph, what is the meaning of the word **initial**?

    a. intermittent

    b. abbreviated

    c. first

    d. clear

Name_____

Into Thin Air
(continued)

Write the correct answer for each question.

10. In the first paragraph, is the term "hooked on flying" a literal or a figurative phrase? _____

_____

11. Is it a fact or an opinion that no one knows what really happened to Earhart? _____

12. What effect did the aerial exhibition have on Earhart's interest in flying?_____

_____

13. What caused people to believe Earhart's plane might have crashed? _____

_____

14. What did Earhart do to pursue her interest in flying the day after she saw the aerial exhibition?

_____

_____

Circle the letter of the best answer.

15. Based on the information in the story, what inference could you make about Amelia Earhart?

    a. She did not adequately prepare for her final flight.

    b. She did not really like flying.

    c. She was adventurous.

    d. She got lost due to bad weather just off of Howland Island.

Related Activities

- Find out about other early aviators — Orville and Wilbur Wright, Charles Lindbergh, and others.

- Look up the Ninety-Nines, a woman pilots' organization that Amelia Earhart formed.

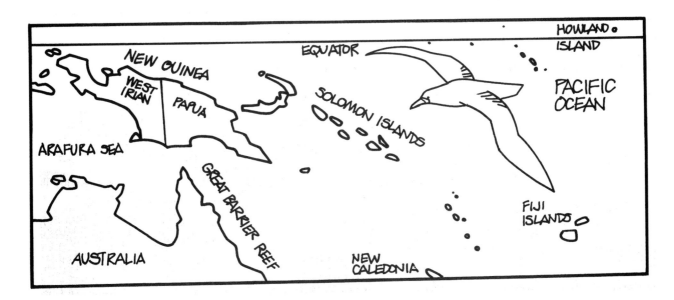

Comprehension Test Prep
© The Learning Works, Inc.

Name_____

The Big Bang

It came out of the sky on June 30, 1908. Large, elongated, and glowing, it raced across the early morning horizon for twenty minutes, observed by only a few awestruck Siberian herdsmen, trappers, and farmers. Then it disappeared over the horizon. It was followed almost immediately by an incredibly violent bang and a column of fire. The bang was so loud that it registered on seismographs around the world. The fire was seen hundreds of miles away and was so intense that it burned land and seared people fifty miles away. The blast was so powerful that it knocked down trees for miles around and nearly derailed an express train four hundred miles to the south. Black rain fell on the country. People in the blast area developed painful sores and blisters.

When scientists arrived to investigate, they expected to see a meteor crater like the one in Arizona, which presumably had been caused by a meteor that had fallen fifty thousand years before. But there was no crater and no meteor, and there were no meteor particles. There was absolutely nothing.

What, then, had caused the big bang? For years afterward, Russian scientists theorized. Some said a meteor had exploded in the air, a theory which accounted for the absence of impact. Others said it was a comet, not a meteor, that collided with Earth.

In 1945, atomic bombs were dropped on Hiroshima and Nagasaki. Scientists noticed that the bombs' impact was similar to the effects of the mighty explosion in Siberia so many years before: a giant cloud, radiation burns, shock waves, and scorched trees were all part of the devastating reaction. New theories emerged. Perhaps the bang was caused by an alien spaceship on its way to Earth. Perhaps the friction of the earth's atmosphere triggered a chain reaction in the ship's atomic fuel, causing an atomic blast.

More recently, scientists have theorized that a tiny "black hole" hit Siberia. Black holes are extremely dense formations of antimatter. In theory, they could pass through the earth in a mere instant. While doing so, they could cause damage similar to that which occurred in Siberia. But this is all theory. Nobody knows what caused the giant bang, and, because no clues remain, it's possible that the truth will never be revealed.

Name_____

The Big Bang
(continued)

Write T if a statement is true. Write F if it is false.

_____1. The main event in this story took place during World War II.

_____2. The main idea of this story is that scientists have many theories.

_____3. Another title for this story could be "What Was It?"

_____4. The fire was so intense that it burned people four hundred miles away.

_____5. The main event in this story occurred in Serbia.

Write the correct answers on the lines.

6. What kind of rain fell after the big bang?_____

7. What word in the third paragraph is a synonym for **crashed**? _____

8. What word in the fourth paragraph is a synonym for **charred**? _____

9. The word **theory** is a noun. Write a verb that means "to think up, create, or formulate theories." _____

10. Repetition is a literary device. What is repeated in the second sentence of the second paragraph?_____

11. Explain whether a theory is a fact or an opinion. _____

_____

12. Describe two effects the big bang had on people in the area.

   a. _____

   b. _____

13. Describe two effects the big bang had on the land.

   a. _____

   b. _____

14. List these theories in the order in which they were formulated to account for the big bang: black hole, meteor, atomic explosion. _____

_____

15. What conclusion can you draw about the way scientists think? _____

_____

_____

_____

_____

Related Activity

• Write a short play, set in the future, in which scientists discover what really caused the big bang.

Comprehension Test Prep
© The Learning Works, Inc.

Name_____

lkers?

A sc...
the ...
feast ...
throu...
ing sp...
these ...
grins ...
comm...
human...

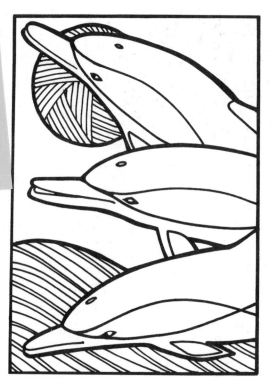

Ma...
series of clicks, chirps, whistles, trills, and moans that dolphins make could be a form of dolphin language. We know, for example, that each dolphin develops a signature whistle, and some feel that with training, dolphins can learn to produce human sounds. Most scientists agree, however, that there is no evidence of a true dolphin language. Whether dolphins can learn to communicate with humans has remained a scientific mystery.

The first challenge is to find a way of "speaking" to dolphins. Sign language has been used in studies with apes, but dolphins do not have hands. Scientists in Florida developed an acoustic language using the sounds of whistles to represent four nouns and three verbs. One dolphin not only learned to identify all seven words, he even mastered 27 different commands made from a combination of the words. For example, when the dolphin heard the whistles for "towel" and "over," it jumped over a towel in the water.

Research is ongoing, and we are learning more about these inquisitive creatures all the time. Who knows — perhaps someday scientists will solve the mystery of whether these "talkative" animals can communicate with us using a language of their own!

Write the correct answer for each question.

1. Where did the research into dolphin communication take place?_____

2. What is the main idea of this story? _____

_____

3. What does the word **aquatic** mean in the title? What other word could you use?_____

_____

4. How fast can dolphins swim? _____

5. In studies to test language abilities of dolphins, how many commands did one dolphin learn?

_____

Name_____

Aquatic Talkers?

(continued)

6. What instrument was used to make "words" dolphins could hear?_____

7. In the second paragraph, what is the meaning of the word **signature**?_____

_____

8. In the third paragraph, what is the meaning of the word **acoustic**? _____

_____

9. In the last paragraph, what is the meaning of the word **inquisitive**? _____

_____

10. In the first sentence, is the "visual feast" a literal or a figurative feast?_____

Circle the letter of the best answer.

11. It is a fact that

    a. Dolphins are the fastest mammals.

    b. Dolphins can learn as many as 27 different commands.

    c. Dolphins are cute.

    d. Dolphins love to communicate with humans.

Write T if a statement is true. Write F if it is false.

_____12. The fact that dolphins seem intelligent causes researchers to want to study them.

_____13. The effect of learning two-word commands is to reinforce the belief that dolphins can learn to communicate with humans.

Write the correct answer for each question.

14. Put the following statements in chronological order, from first to last:

_____a. The dolphin jumped over the towel.

_____b. Researchers assigned whistle sounds to four nouns and three verbs.

_____c. The researcher blew the whistle with the command "towel"-"over."

_____d. Researchers decided to study whether dolphins could learn simple commands.

15. What conclusions can you draw about whether dolphins can communicate with humans?

_____

_____

Related Activities

- Search the Internet to find out about current research into dolphin communication.

- Find out about the Dolphin/Child Program that uses dolphins to help people with special needs.

Comprehension Test Prep
© The Learning Works, Inc.

Name_____

A Mystery Solved?

How would you like to solve an ancient mystery? Although this mystery is at least 40,000 years old, scientists have been aware of it only since 1856. In that year, some bones were discovered in the Neander Valley in western Germany, east of Dusseldorf. Labeled Neanderthal because of the place in which they were found, these bones were first thought to be the remains of some unfortunate army deserter. Upon closer examination, they were identified as the fossils of a prehistoric human, one of many similar beings who roamed throughout what is now Europe and southwest Asia between 100,000 and 40,000 years ago.

Since this find, archaeologists have unearthed many clues about how these ancient people lived. For example, we know that Neanderthals dwelt in caves, had discovered fire, and were skilled at chipping stone tools. In addition, we know that they lived by gathering and by hunting behemoths — woolly mammoths, giant bison, and giant rhinos.

If we know so much, you may be asking, what is the mystery? The mystery is not *what* Neanderthals hunted, but *how.* They had stone blades, and they may have had spears; but bows and arrows had not yet been developed. Thus, their weapons were short-range and entirely dependent for power on the strength of the people using them. Yet somehow, Neanderthal hunters were able to employ these weapons successfully to kill their formidable prey.

Clues to the solution of this mystery can be read in Neanderthal bones, which indicate that these prehistoric people were strong, quick, and able to swing arm over arm. Their massive joints connote tremendous strength, as well as the ability to start, stop, and change direction suddenly. Furthermore, their hands were very large and powerful, with a much wider finger spread than is found on modern human hands. And although Neanderthals lived on the open plains, they had shoulders that rendered them capable of brachiation. On the basis of these and other clues, some scientists have theorized that Neanderthal hunters chased their prey and killed what they caught in hands-on combat.

There is less evidence to support another theory, which suggests that Neanderthals may have been more intelligent than they were, at first, given credit for being. Scientists who subscribe to this theory believe that these prehistoric people may have studied the habits and habitats of the incredibly powerful animals they hunted and used not only strength but cunning to overcome them.

Is one of these theories the answer to this 40,000-year-old mystery or does the solution remain to be found?

Name_____

A Mystery Solved?
(continued)

Write the correct answer for each question.

1. Since when have scientists been trying to solve the mystery of how Neanderthals hunted?

   _____

2. What is the main idea of this story? _____

   _____

3. Write another possible title for the story. _____

4. During what time period did Neanderthals live? _____

   _____

5. What weapons did Neanderthals use to kill animals?_____

6. Where were the first Neanderthal fossils found?_____

   _____

7. What does **prehistoric** mean? _____

8. What is a **behemoth**? _____

9. What does **brachiate** mean? _____

   _____

10. A **simile** is the comparison of two unlike objects, often using the word **like** or **as**. Think of a comparison and complete the following as a simile: A Neanderthal man chasing a woolly mammoth was like_____

    _____

11. Is it fact or opinion that a Neanderthal killed his prey in hands-on combat? _____

    How do you know? _____

    _____

12. What would be the effect of having massive finger joints and fingers that could spread very far apart? _____

    _____

13. What caused scientists to name these prehistoric humans Neanderthals? _____

    _____

14. Which came first in weapon development, stone blades or bows and arrows?_____

15. In which part of the world did Neanderthals live? _____

    _____

Related Activity

- Visit a museum and look at the displays of Neanderthal life. Give a speech to the class, describing the Neanderthal's anatomy, home life, clothing, weapons, and art.

Comprehension Test Prep
© The Learning Works, Inc.

Name_____

26.218

Marathoner, a twentieth-century word, is defined as "a person who runs in a marathon." In 490 B.C., the Greeks won an important victory over the invading Persians on a plain called Marathon. A Greek runner was commanded to carry the news to Athens. Alas, as he completed the twenty-four-mile run, this courier collapsed and died. But he won everlasting glory as the original marathoner. And *marathon* has found its place in history as the name of a long-distance, cross-country race.

More than 2,300 years after that Greek messenger's death, the marathon race was revived. The 1896 Olympic Games featured a long-distance foot race across 24 miles. In 1908, the Olympics were held in Great Britain. When the marathon course was laid out, it was lengthened to 26.218 miles so that members of the British royal family would not have to leave their box to see the runners. Marathon races have been 26.218 miles long ever since.

Today, hundreds of official marathons are run throughout the world every year. The most famous marathons in the United States are held in Boston, New York City, Chicago, and Honolulu. There is even a race in Colorado that goes up and down Pike's Peak!

What is considered a good time for completing a marathon run? It varies greatly. At seventy-one years of age, Mavis Lindgren ran a marathon in 4 hours, 42 minutes, and 49 seconds. Frank Shorter won the 1972 Olympic marathon in 2:12:20. In 1999, Khalid Khannouchi of Morocco held the men's world record at 2:05:42, and Tegla Loroupe of Kenya set a new women's record with 2:20:42.

Modern marathoners come in all ages, sizes, and physical conditions. It is no longer unusual to see a person in a wheelchair zipping across the finish line. Marathoners are a far cry from the originator of the sport. That Greek courier had to run to deliver an urgent message. Nowadays, marathoners run for their health, the mental and physical challenge, the spirit of competition, and just plain fun. Furthermore, they're all amateurs: they run by choice.

Name_____

26.218

(continued)

Circle the letter of the best answer.

1. This story covers events that occurred
   a. from 490 B.C. to A.D. 1896.
   b. from A.D. 1896 to A.D. 1972.
   c. from 490 B.C. to the present.

2. This story is about
   a. runners.
   b. the Olympics.
   c. marathoners.

3. The title refers to
   a. Khalid Khannouchi's time.
   b. the distance covered by a modern marathon course.
   c. the distance run by an unknown Greek messenger.

4. According to the story, the women's world record was set by
   a. Tegla Lourope.
   b. Mavis Lindgren.
   c. Grete Waitz.

5. The Greek courier described in the story ran from Marathon to
   a. Sparta.
   b. Athens.
   c. Pike's Peak.

Write the correct answer for each question.

6. Who won the 1972 Olympic marathon? _____

7. Write out in words what 2:08:13 means. _____

   _____

8. How is a courier in ancient Greece different from a marathon runner of today? _____

   _____

   _____

   _____

Comprehension Test Prep
© The Learning Works, Inc.

Name_____

26.218

(continued)

Write the correct answer for each question.

9. The suffix **-thon** is added to words to indicate an event of great length or requiring unusual endurance. Using this suffix, write words meaning "a long walking contest" and "a video game contest."

   a. _____   b. _____

10. The last sentence of the story is, "Furthermore they're all amateurs; they run by choice."

    To what other information in the story does this sentence allude? _____

    _____

11. Is it fact or opinion that a Colorado marathon goes up and down Pike's Peak? _____

12. What was the effect of the Greek messenger's 24-mile run? _____

    _____

13. What was the reason for his run? _____

    _____

    _____

14. Describe the sequence of events that resulted in the present marathon distance of 26.218

    miles. _____

    _____

    _____

    _____

15. Why don't modern marathoners collapse and die as the Greek messenger did? _____

    _____

    _____

    _____

    _____

Related Activity

- Write a short story told from the point of view of a marathoner as he or she runs the grueling race.

Name_____

Two Kinds of Skiing

Skiing is a popular sport throughout the world. Approximately five hundred years ago, however, skiing wasn't a sport but a matter of life and death.

Swedes, Finns, and Norwegians used wooden slats, called skis, in warfare. The skis helped speed them to battle. An interesting feature of these early skis was that one of each pair was seven feet long and the other was only four feet long. Scandinavian soldiers skied on the long one and pushed with the short one.

Today, there are two main kinds of skiing: Alpine, or downhill skiing, which first became popular in the Alps, and Nordic, or cross-country skiing. One of the most graceful sights in Alpine skiing is slalom skiing, in which a skier smoothly negotiates a zig-zag course between a series of poles or other obstacles. Slalom skiing has spawned an offshoot, called hotdog skiing, in which the skier performs tricks.

Although slalom may seem like trick skiing, it isn't. To wend your way down a heavily forested mountain trail, either you learn to maneuver gracefully, or you end up in a head-to-trunk confrontation with a tree! But the tricks in hotdog skiing are not necessary to get down a mountain. They include such feats as somersaulting in the air during a jump, jumping over barrels placed on the ski path, and doing a split while airborne.

Nordic, or cross-country, skiing must have been the method used to reach those ancient battles. This sport no longer requires one short and one long ski. Nordic skiers can travel quite rapidly over flat land, up hills, down hills, and around obstacles. Some people say Nordic skiing is less spectacular than Alpine skiing, but it is also much safer and more beneficial to the development of physical fitness.

Sound like fun? Get yourself a pair of skis, some poles, boots, and warm clothing; then, most importantly, find yourself a mountain or countryside, white with snow.

Comprehension Test Prep
© The Learning Works, Inc.

Name_____

Two Kinds of Skiing

(continued)

Write the correct answer for each question.

1. What verb tense is used throughout most of this story?_____

   What does the use of this tense indicate about the information in the story? _____

   _____

2. What is the main idea of this story? _____

   _____

3. Supply two possible titles for this story.

   a. _____

   b. _____

4. How long was the short ski worn by Scandinavian soldiers? _____

5. Where did downhill skiing first become popular? _____

6. What is another name for Nordic skiing? _____

7. What is a slalom? _____

   _____

8. What word in the third paragraph means "produced; brought forth"?_____

9. Write three non-hyphenated compound words that appear in the third paragraph.

   a. _____ b. _____ c. _____

10. Explain the phrase, "head-to-trunk confrontation with a tree." What is the writer saying?

   _____

   _____

Name_____

Two Kinds of Skiing
(continued)

Circle the letter of the best answer.

11. It is a fact that
    a. Scandinavian soldiers once wore skis.
    b. Alpine skiing is beautiful to watch.
    c. hotdog skiing is silly.

12. The purpose of slalom skiing is to
    a. look graceful.
    b. avoid obstacles in your path.
    c. perform fancy tricks.

13. For the Scandinavian soldiers, the effect of pushing with a short ski was
    a. moving forward on the long ski.
    b. lengthening the long ski.
    c. moving backward on the long ski.

14. Alpine skiing developed
    a. after hotdog skiing.
    b. before Nordic skiing.
    c. before hotdog skiing.

15. There are probably more injuries relative to the number of participants in
    a. cross-country skiing.
    b. downhill skiing.
    c. hotdog skiing.

Related Activity

• Draw two pictures, one of an Alpine skier and one of a Nordic skier. Label the clothing worn and the equipment used by each one.

Comprehension Test Prep
© The Learning Works, Inc.

Name_____

Night of Dreams

It was the busiest night of track and field at the Sydney Games in Australia—September 5, 2000. Cathy Freeman, a 27-year-old Australian and Aborigine (Australia's indigenous people), focused on the start of the final 400-meter race. She realized that with this race she carried not only her own dreams but the hopes of her nation and the Aboriginal people.

The starting gun fired, and Freeman shot out. She and Lorraine Graham of Jamaica were the two favorites. Throughout most of the race, they were neck-and-neck. Then, with 20 meters to go, Freeman pulled away and with a few additional strides, crossed the finish line, the first Aborigine to win an individual Olympic gold medal.

Overwhelmed with the excitement of victory, Freeman sat down on the track and pulled off her shoes. Then she got up, grabbed an Aboriginal flag and an Australian flag, and took her victory lap bare-footed, just as she learned to run as a child along dried river banks in central Australia. After the medal ceremony, she walked to the stands and gave a bouquet of flowers to her mother. "This has been a dream since I was a little girl and it's why I'm emotional," she said.

Just ten days before, Freeman had been chosen to light the Olympic flame at the opening ceremony of the Sydney Games. Choosing Freeman, a champion of Aboriginal rights, to light the Olympic flame symbolized the country's efforts to heal the wounds over the treatment of its indigenous people: Thousands of Aborigines had been massacred after Australia was colonized by white settlers, and Aborigines couldn't even vote until 1967. Freeman will never know who her grandfather or great-grandmother were because of the Australian government's forced removal of about 100,000 Aboriginal children from their homes from 1910 until the 1970s.

Freeman, with obvious emotion, jogged up a flight of stairs, stepped into a pool and touched the torch to the water, creating a circle of flame. As the ring of fire encircled her, a cauldron rose around her, and reached the top of the stadium on a track that followed the course of a waterfall. Cathy Freeman, who told Aboriginal children, "Be proud and strong, and like me you can do whatever you want if you set your heart on it," truly was a role model for her people and country.

Write the correct answer for each question.

1. Where did the events described in this story take place?_____

_____

2. What is the main idea of the story?_____

_____

3. Explain the meaning of the title of the story. _____

_____

Name_____

Night of Dreams

(continued)

Circle the letter(s) of the best answer.

4. Which flag or flags did Cathy Freeman carry when she made her victory lap around Olympic stadium?

   a. Aboriginal flag

   b. United Nations flag

   c. Australian flag

   d. Olympic flag

Write the correct answer for each question.

5. When did the Aboriginal people obtain the right to vote in Australia? _____

6. Who was Freeman's main competitor in the 400-meter final? _____

7. What does **indigenous** mean? _____

8. What is a synonym for **cauldron**? _____

9. What is a **role model**? _____

10. Cathy Freeman was a sports champion. What does it mean to be a "champion of Aboriginal rights?"_____

   _____

11. Is it fact or opinion that Cathy Freeman will never know her grandfather? _____

12. What caused the Australian Olympic committee to ask Freeman to light the Olympic flame?

   _____

   _____

13. What effect did the forced removal of 100,000 Aboriginal children have on Freeman and her family? _____

14. Put these events in chronological order: running the 400-meter race; lighting the Olympic flame; running along dried river banks in central Australia; presenting flowers to her mother.

   _____

   _____

15. In your opinion, why does Cathy Freeman strive to be a role model for Aboriginal children?

   _____

   _____

Related Activity

- Learn about these Aboriginal athletes and write a short biography on one of them: Mark Ella, rugby star; Lionel Rose, boxing star; Evonne Goolagongck (Goolagong), tennis star; Nova Peris-Kneebone, hockey gold medalist.

Comprehension Test Prep
© The Learning Works, Inc.

Name_____

What a Game!

On Dominion Day, Canadians celebrate the day Canada became a nation. On that same day, July 1, 1867, another important event occurred in Canada. Parliament designated lacrosse as the national sport.

Native Americans probably had played lacrosse thousands of years before the English and French reached the shores of the continent. It was the French who named the game *la crosse*, meaning "the staff, or long-handled stick," because the game stick resembled a bishop's staff of office.

What a wild game the original version must have been! First, there were few rules. There was no set size for either team. One game might have just a few players on each side, while another might have thousands! The playing field had no limits or dimensions. Wherever the ball went, the players followed. Goals might be a few hundred yards or several miles apart, depending on what the players decided.

Some of the unique elements of lacrosse were lost in the 1800s, when William George Beers, a Montreal dentist, drew up the first written rules for the game. He also helped form lacrosse teams throughout Canada. By 1867, it was truly that country's national sport.

Today, lacrosse is usually played on an outdoor field with ten players per team. The object of the game is to score goals at the opponent's end of the field. Players are not permitted to touch the ball with their hands. Instead, they scoop it up in the small net baskets of their lacrosse sticks. They use a technique called "cradling" to keep the ball in their sticks as they run toward the goal.

Although lacrosse may no longer be as unconventional a game as when the Native Americans played it, this spirited sport is to Canada what baseball is to the United States.

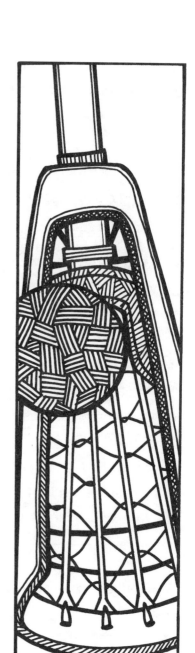

Write the correct answer for each question.

1. What time period does this article cover? _____

   _____

2. What is the main idea of this article? _____

   _____

   _____

Name_____

What a Game!
(continued)

3. Why might "Who Needs Rules?" be a good title for this article? _____

   _____

   _____

4. Who first wrote down the rules for lacrosse? _____

5. When did lacrosse become the national sport of Canada?_____

   _____

6. What group of people probably played lacrosse thousands of years before the Canadians?

   _____

7. What is an **opponent**? _____

   _____

8. What does **resembled** mean? _____

9. What part of speech is **unconventional**, and what does it mean? _____

   _____

10. An **analogy** is a relationship or correspondence between one pair of terms that serves as the basis for the creation of another pair or as a means of explaining the relationship between members of a second pair. The sixth paragraph contains an analogy.

    Write it here. _____

    _____

    What does this analogy mean?_____

    _____

Write T if a statement is true. Write F if it is false.

_____11. It is an opinion that a Montreal dentist first wrote down rules for a game called lacrosse.

_____12. Originally, the lack of formal rules made lacrosse a lively and unpredictable game.

_____13. One of the effects of there being no formal rules for lacrosse was that the teams varied greatly in size.

_____14. Native Americans called their game *la crosse*.

_____15. Formal game rules are probably a relatively recent trend in sports.

Related Activity

- Polo and golf are also very old games. Read about one of these games, and write a brief (250- to 300-word) report on its history and development.

Comprehension Test Prep
© The Learning Works, Inc.

Name_____

Mush Against Death

Imagine traveling over snow and ice on foot, accompanied by a dog team pulling a sled. This is mushing, and it is considered a sport by many people. Mushing contests are held in many places where there is a combination of snow, people, and a breed of dogs called huskies.

Diphtheria is a deadly contagious disease. This illness, which affects the mucous membranes of the throat, often results in suffocation and death. Today, the disease has almost disappeared, because children are given antidiphtheria inoculations.

What, you may ask, do mushing and diphtheria have to do with each other?

In January of 1925, the world's most important mushing event took place in Alaska. The weather was bad — fifty degrees below zero — with winds that screamed at eighty miles an hour. In addition, there was never-ending night because the sun never rises above the Arctic Circle in January. The dogsled race stretched from Nenana to Nome, a distance of 674 miles.

Normally this run took fifteen days by dogsled, the only available means of transportation. But this time, it could not — must not — take fifteen days. Diphtheria had struck the town of Nome, and two thousand lives were at stake. The antitoxin that could save those lives was loaded onto a dogsled at Nenana, and the race against death began.

Nine dogs and one man started out that day, and relay teams were organized along the way. It was so cold that the dogs often froze and had to be carried on the sled. It was so dark that it was difficult to see where to step. Snowdrifts were waist high. The ice was as slick as glass. The dogs' feet bled. The men's hands froze to the sled. But they never gave up.

These hardy Alaskans represented many different nationalities — American, British, Eskimo, Finnish, Indian, Irish, Italian, Russian, and Swedish. They all had one common goal — to get the serum to Nome. Most men ran a relay leg of 20 miles. One man ran 150 miles! With cooperative efforts of the mushers, they got the serum to Nome in less than half the usual time — and thus saved many lives.

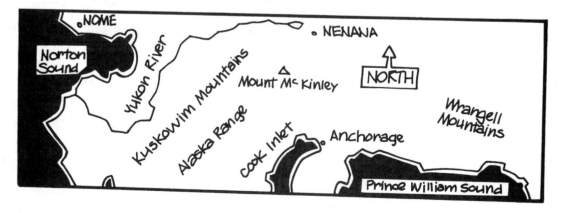

Name_____

Mush Against Death
(continued)

Write the correct answer for each question.

1. When did the events in this story take place?_____

2. What is the main idea of this story? _____

   _____

   _____

3. What would be another appropriate title for this story?_____

   _____

Write the letter of the correct answer on the line in front of each number.

_____4. The deadly disease was   A. antitoxin.

_____5. The serum was a/an   B. hardy.

_____6. The serum was carried by   C. diphtheria.

_____7. Someone who is capable of withstanding fatigue   D. mushed.
and hardship is said to be

_____8. The men who traveled on foot alongside the dogs   E. dogsled.

Comprehension Test Prep
© The Learning Works, Inc.

Name_____

Mush Against Death
(continued)

Write the correct answer for each question.

9. You can infer what an **antitoxin** is from this story and from what you know about prefixes and root words. What is an antitoxin?_____

   _____

   _____

10. In the fifth paragraph, this mushing event is termed "the race against death." Is this expression literal or figurative? _____

    Explain your answer. _____

    _____

    _____

11. Is it fact or opinion that diphtheria is a deadly contagious disease that affects the mucous membranes? _____

12. What caused the men to travel by dogsled?_____

    _____

    _____

13. What was the effect of the race?_____

    _____

    _____

14. Where did the race begin and where did it end? _____

    _____

15. What conclusion can you draw about the limits to which people will push themselves?

    _____

    _____

    _____

Related Activity

- Boating is usually considered a sport, but in Dunkirk, France, from May 26 until June 4, 1940, boating became a matter of life or death. Read about what took place during these ten days, and then write a story based on what you learn in a style similar to that used for "Mush Against Death."

Name_____

The Last Lap

Stan was one of four in the single-file echelon. He was in front, moving as fast and as hard as he could, watching the road ahead and catching an occasional glimpse of his shoes. "Sissy slippers," his sister had called the shoes, saying that they resembled her ballet slippers. "Well, perhaps they do," thought Stan, "but ballet slippers are not reinforced with steel. Nor do ballet slippers have cleats." Stan felt the powerful wind resistance as he put every ounce of his strength into maintaining the lead. The ground slipped away behind him at fifty miles per hour. Then, his energy spent, he dropped back. Frank took the lead.

Now taking advantage of the slipstream, Stan was able to expend one-quarter less energy. Riding behind the three other racers, he encountered less air resistance. The four riders in his echelon had broken away from the mass start of about fifty competitors. The course itself was only two miles around, but it was a fifty-mile race, which meant twenty-five laps. To win, breaking away was essential. If you got stuck in the field, you could be blocked or knocked down.

Stan watched Frank give up the lead and slip into fourth place. Now Stan was third in the breakaway group. The members of the group had agreed, explicitly and implicitly, to leave the field and help one another open and maintain a gap. Such a breakaway group formed an echelon — a staggered line in which the riders took turns in the lead, while other group members rode downwind of the leader.

Stan saw the finish line ahead. This was the critical moment. He had to break away from the group to cross the line first. Now! The echelon broke up as the four riders pulled out and pedaled with all of their strength toward the finish!

Write the correct answer for each question.

1. What type of race is this story about?_____

2. What is the main idea of this story? _____

    _____

    _____

3. What does the title indicate? _____

    _____

4. What is the name of the rider who is in first place in the echelon when Stan is in fourth place?

    _____

5. Describe Stan's shoes. _____

    _____

    _____

Comprehension Test Prep
© The Learning Works, Inc.

Name_____

The Last Lap
(continued)

6. Briefly describe the length of the race and the type of course on which the riders are competing. _____

_____

7. In this story, what is an **echelon**? _____

_____

8. In this story, what does **breaking away** mean? _____

_____

9. **Breakaway** is a compound word. Read each definition, then write the compound word beginning with **break** that matches the definition.

   a. A highly dangerous speed is called a _____ speed.

   b. A violent or forceful escape from prison is called a _____ .

   c. The first meal of the day after a night without food is _____ .

10. "The ground slipped away behind him at fifty miles per hour." Is this statement literal or figurative? What does it mean?_____

_____

_____

11. What does Stan's sister think of her brother's shoes? _____

_____

12. What is the effect of being behind the leader in a breakaway group? _____

_____

_____

_____

13. What causes the cycling group to break up on the last lap? _____

_____

14. In what position is Stan at the beginning of the story? _____

_____

15. What conclusions can you draw about the physical abilities of the people in a breakaway group? _____

_____

_____

Related Activity

- Write a short story about someone who is participating in a particular sport. Do not reveal immediately what the sport is, but give your reader clues as the story develops.

Answer Key

Pages 9-11 • Ninety North!

1. 1905 - 50 = 1855
2. Robert Peary wanted to be the first man to reach the North Pole; and, after six failures, he finally succeeded.
3. "Ninety North" was Peary's motto. It was derived from "90 degrees north," the latitude designation given to the North Pole.
4. Pearyaksoah; "Big Peary"
5. 70 degrees below zero
6. He was in Greenland.
7. birth
8. persistent; unrelenting; without stopping
9. seek; hunt or look for
10. figuratively
    Immortality means "the state or condition of living forever; not dying." Peary achieved immortality figuratively in that his name will live forever in the annals of history. He did not achieve immortality literally in that his body did not live forever: he died in 1920.
11. Peary felt that reaching the North Pole was a significant feat, one well worth accomplishing; the Eskimos thought that the North Pole was just another barren, cold, snowy place and saw no particular reason to go there.
12. Peary turned back because his men and dogs were starving; the weather had defeated them.
13. Peary was disheartened. He believed that he would not reach the North Pole; he felt that he had made his last attempt and that he had failed.
14. Maine, Nicaragua, Greenland, North Pole
15. Peary was determined, adventuresome, accustomed to hardship, and considerate of the people and animals with which he worked.

Pages 12-13 • Lifeboat Aquarius

1. They began on April 13, 1970, and ended more than eighty hours later, on April 17, 1970.
2. When an explosion crippled their spacecraft and rendered it incapable of generating power or supplying oxygen, three Apollo astronauts stayed alive by using their lunar module, called *Aquarius*, as a lifeboat.
3. Answers will vary.
4. *Apollo 13*
5. Haise, Lovell, and Swigert
6. 18,000 miles per hour
7. abandoned

8. enormous
9. lifeboat; without; withstand
10. For more than three days, the men lived in this lifeboat much like three hermit crabs squeezed into one shell.
11. fact
12. effects
13. causes
14. when
15. perfectly

Pages 14-15 • Frozen in Time

1. 500 years ago
2. Scientists search for ice mummies and study them to learn about the past.
3. Answers will vary.
4. Scientists found ice mummies—two girls and one boy—and statues, textiles, and pottery, believed to be offerings to the Inca gods.
5. The Andes in Argentina
6. Dr. Johan Reinhard
7. Archaeology is the study of human life and culture in past times.
8. An offering is a gift to a God or deity to show worship or devotion.
9. Bacteria is any of numerous unicellular microorganisms occurring in a wide variety of forms, existing either as free-living organisms or as parasites. Synonym: germs.
10. The scientists had a difficult time coping or struggling against the strong winds which felt like they were thrashing or beating upon them.
11. opinion
12. Freezing halts the decay caused by bacteria and fungi.
13. He read that Incan ruins had been found there.
14. Scientists climb Mt. Llullaillaco; scientists dig through frozen rock; a mummy of a child is found in the Andes; scientists use DNA to study the mummies.
15. Answers will vary. Some reasons might be that he likes the challenge, finds the experience an unique one, enjoys the beauty of the mountains, or is fascinated by the history of the region.

Comprehension Test Prep
© The Learning Works, Inc.

Answer Key

(continued)

Pages 16-17 • Life on the Moon

1. 1835
2. An unscrupulous reporter used fabricated accounts of life on the moon to boost the circulation of a newspaper called the *New York Sun.*
3. There really was no life on the moon.
4. Sir John Herschel
5. January 18, 1835
6. Richard Adams Locke
7. subsequent
8. an act intended to trick or dupe someone into accepting a fake as genuine or believing that a lie is true
9. circulation, circulate; or imagination, imagine
10. the most marvelous or amazing among a group of marvelous or amazing things
11. T
12. T
13. F
14. F
15. T

Pages 18-19 • They Traveled Far

1. b
2. c
3. c
4. a
5. b
6. eighteen years old
7. pen name
8. enormous; gigantic; huge
9. adventuresome; newspaper
10. travel around the world
11. opinion
12. He was so impressed by her writing that he hired her to be a reporter for the newspaper.
13. She was incensed by an article entitled "What Girls Are Good For" that had been printed in the paper, and she felt compelled to respond in a letter defending the rights of women.

14. Any four of the following: She became a champion ice skater, sold automobiles, drove across the country, became a stunt pilot, and worked as an actress, a writer, and a radio commentator.
15. Both Nellie Bly and Blanche Stuart Scott were courageous and enjoyed a challenge. Neither one of them was inhibited by society's ideas about what they should do, be, or become. Each of the women preferred to chart her own course.

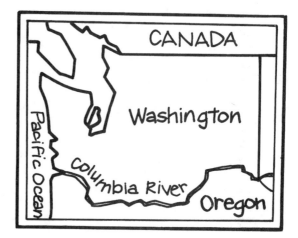

Pages 20-21 • From Failure to Success

1. 1807
2. Simon Fraser set out to explore the northern waters of the Columbia River but instead ended up exploring what became known as Fraser River.
3. Answers will vary.
4. D
5. C
6. A
7. E
8. B
9. vied; vie
10. "Happily, Fraser's 'failure' turned into an unexpected success."
11. fact
12. The North West Company of Canada had sent Fraser to explore this area.
13. Fraser explored the mouth of a river, other than the Columbia, and this river was subsequently named for him.
14. Meriwether Lewis and William Clark
15. He was tough, persistent, dedicated, and committed.

Answer Key

(continued)

Pages 22-24 • To the Root of the Mystery of Clever Hans

1. Germany
2. c
3. Root can mean "the bottom of" or it can be a reference to Hans' ability to solve square root math problems.
4. Herr von Osten believed animals are as smart as humans.
5. They had Herr von Osten leave the room.
6. He couldn't solve the problems when no one in the room knew the answers.
7. theory
8. stumped
9. slight
10. figurative
11. fact
12. They thought he was giving the horse the answers.
13. Scientists realized the importance of double blind experiments.
14. d, c, a, b
15. There is no reason to think Herr von Osten was trying to trick anyone. He didn't realize he was giving Hans hints to the answers. He even left the room so scientists could test whether he was cheating.

Pages 25-26 • The Disappearing Emerald

1. past
2. lady; tray; jewels; emerald
3. summarizes
4. dough
5. ermine
6. thirteen
7. comforting; calming
8. carefully
9. hood and wink
   to blindfold; to hide; to deceive by false appearance
10. figurative; If the jeweler's heart had literally stopped, he would have died.
11. opinion

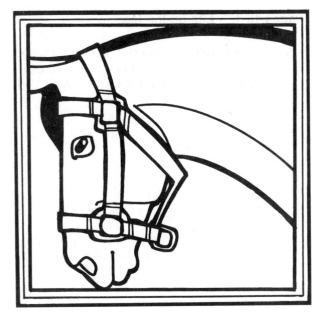

12. The lady bumped the tray in which the stones were stored.
13. The falling stones and the accompanying commotion startled the dog, and he began to bark.
14. eagerness, jubilation, dismay, suspicion
15. winter
    The lady is wearing a fur-trimmed cloak and carrying a fur muff.

Pages 27-29 • Into Thin Air

1. 1897 (she was 40 in 1937)
2. c
3. No one ever found Amelia Earhart or her plane. She disappeared "into thin air."
4. She thought it was "not at all interesting."
5. Miami, Florida
6. She landed in New Guinea and was lost en route to Howland Island.
7. heightened
8. dangerous
9. c
10. figurative
11. It is a fact. There are many theories, but no one really knows what happened.
12. It sparked her interest in flying.
13. They lost radio contact with her and never found her or her plane.
14. She went up in an airplane for a ride over Los Angeles.
15. c

Answer Key

(continued)

Pages 30-31 • The Big Bang
1. F
2. F
3. T
4. F
5. F
6. black rain
7. collided
8. scorched
9. theorize
10. the word *no* is repeated.
11. A theory is an opinion. It is an effort to explain the unknown on the basis of what is known or can be observed.
12. Any two of the following: It filled people with awe. It burned people. It caused people to develop painful sores and blisters.
13. Any two of the following: It burned the land. It knocked down trees. It caused the earth to shake. It caused black rain.
14. meteor, atomic explosion, black hole
15. Scientists look at facts and interpret events in light of what they already know. When they learn something new, they take another look at unexplained events to see if their new knowledge can be used to explain an old event.

Pages 32-33 • Aquatic Talkers?
1. Florida
2. Some people think dolphins might be able to communicate with humans.
3. Aquatic means "living in the water." Other possible words include marine, watery, or water-dwelling.
4. 25 mph (40 km)
5. 27
6. a whistle
7. distinctive
8. related to sound
9. curious
10. figurative
11. b
12. T
13. T
14. d, b, c, a
15. Although dolphins do not seem to have their own language, they appear to be able to learn simple words and commands. It is possible that they can be trained to communicate with humans.

Pages 34-35 • A Mystery Solved?
1. Scientists have been trying to solve this mystery since they discovered bones of these prehistoric humans in 1856.
2. It is a mystery to scientists how Neanderthals managed to kill the giant animals they hunted.
3. Answers will vary.
4. between 100,000 and 40,000 years ago
5. stone blades and possibly spears
6. in the Neander Valley in western Germany, east of Dusseldorf
7. living in or belonging to the time before written history
8. an animal of monstrous size or power
9. to progress as a result of swinging by the arms and grasping one handhold after another
10. Answers will vary.
11. opinion
    You know that it is an opinion because the story says this explanation is what some scientists have theorized.
12. Your hands would be very strong and able to grip large objects easily.
13. Their bones were found in the Neander Valley.
14. stone blades
15. They lived in what is now Europe and southwest Asia.

Answer Key

(continued)

Pages 36-38 • 26.218

1. c
2. c
3. b
4. a
5. b
6. Frank Shorter
7. two hours, eight minutes, and thirteen seconds
8. A courier in ancient Greece delivered important messages in person by running the distance between the sender and the receiver. In other words, running was his job. Today, running is a sport or form of recreation. It is hard work, but it is not a job.
9. walkathon; video game-a-thon
10. Greek couriers, or messengers, were runners by command, not by choice.
11. fact
12. According to legend, he collapsed and died.
13. He was commanded to carry back to Athens the news of Greece's victory over the Persians at Marathon.
14. The 1896 Olympic Games introduced a foot race of 24 miles. When the Olympics were held in Great Britain in 1908, the marathon course was lengthened to this distance so that members of the British royal family would not have to leave their box to see the runners.
15. They are probably better trained; they are not exhausted from fighting a battle; they are probably better fed; and they are supplied with liquids along the course so that they do not become dehydrated.

Pages 39-41 • Two Kinds of Skiing

1. present tense
   Use of the present tense indicates that the information is current.
2. There are two main kinds of skiing — Alpine and Nordic.
3. Answers will vary.
4. four feet
5. in the Alps
6. cross-country skiing
7. a race against time over a course that zigzags between upright obstacles
8. spawned

9. Order may vary.
   a. downhill
   b. offshoot
   c. hotdog
10. If you do not learn how to ski around obstacles such as trees, you may crash headfirst into one.
11. a
12. b
13. a
14. c
15. c

Pages 42-43 • Night of Dreams

1. Australia
2. Freeman, a proud, strong, focused Aboriginal woman, saw her dreams come true when she lit the Olympic flame and won the gold medal for the 400-meter race.
3. The 400-meter race took place at night and, by winning it, Freeman realized her dreams for herself, her people, and her nation.
4. a, c
5. 1967
6. Lorraine Graham of Jamaica
7. the original people of an area; native
8. a large kettle or vat
9. a person of high standards who sets a good example for others
10. to fight for, defend, or support the civil rights of the Aboriginal people
11. fact
12. They wanted a symbol of the country's efforts to heal wounds over the treatment of its indigenous people.
13. It meant she would never know some of her family members.
14. running along dry riverbanks; lighting the Olympic flame; running the 400-meter race; presenting flowers to her mother
15. She knows the hardships her people face, especially the children, and wants to encourage them to be proud and strong and set goals for themselves.

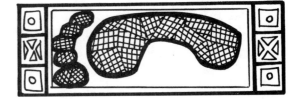

Answer Key

(continued)

Pages 44-45 • What a Game!

1. from the beginnings of lacrosse to the present
2. Lacrosse, a game first played by Native Americans, has become the national sport of Canada.
3. This title would be appropriate because the article explains that lacrosse was played without formal, written rules for perhaps thousands of years.
4. a Montreal dentist named William George Beers
5. on July 1, 1867; Dominion Day
6. Native Americans
7. one who opposes, or goes against another, usually in a game or contest, but sometimes in an argument, election, or fight; adversary; antagonist
8. looked like; was similar to
9. adjective; being out of the ordinary
10. ". . . this spirited sport is to Canada what baseball is to the United States." Just as baseball is the national pastime of the United States, lacrosse is the national sport of Canada.
11. F
12. T
13. T
14. F
15. T

Pages 46-48 • Mush Against Death

1. 1925
2. The greatest mushing event ever held was a race not against other contestants but against time, the weather, disease, and death.
3. Answers will vary.
4. C
5. A
6. E
7. B
8. D
9. A toxin is something that is poisonous; an antitoxin is a substance that fights against or neutralizes toxins.
10. literal; The longer it took for the antitoxin to reach Nome, the greater the number of people who would be stricken by the disease and die. Thus, the race was literally against time and death.
11. fact

12. Because of the weather and the terrain, dogsled was the only feasible means of transportation.
13. The antitoxin was delivered in less than half the usual time, so more people were saved.
14. It began in Nenana, Alaska, and ended in Nome, Alaska.
15. People will push themselves to perform superhuman feats of strength and endurance when their lives or the lives of others are at stake.

Pages 49-50 • The Last Lap

1. a bicycle race
2. Stan has ridden as a member of a four-person breakaway group; and now, during the last lap, it is time for the members of the group to make their individual sprints to the finish line.
3. The title indicates that the action in this story builds toward the last lap which is the focus of the end of the story.
4. Frank
5. Stan's shoes are made of soft leather like the leather used for ballet slippers, but they have cleats and are reinforced with steel.
6. The race is fifty miles long. The participating cyclists pedal twenty-five laps around a two-mile course.
7. a line of cyclists, each riding at a certain distance behind and downwind of the cyclist ahead
8. pedaling fast and hard to move away from the mass of competitors bunched together at the beginning of the race.
9. a. breakneck
   b. breakout
   c. breakfast
10. figurative; Stan was moving over the ground at fifty miles per hour. As he looked down, the ground appeared to move beneath him but was actually standing still.
11. She calls them "sissy slippers."
12. Because you encounter less wind resistance, pedaling is easier, and you can conserve energy for the final break toward the finish line.
13. They break up to sprint toward the finish line.
14. the lead position in a breakaway group
15. They must be equally strong, agile, and physically fit. Each one must be capable of pedaling in the lead, and all must be able to move out of the way of the many other cyclists around them at the start of the race.